Acceptin

A D aughter's

Post Traumatic Stress Disorder

**After military service ends,
inner wounds need healing.**

Quynn Elizabeth is the only daughter of a two-time Viet Nam combat veteran, and granddaughter of a WW2 Air Force pilot shot down over the Pacific ocean. After her father's lonely death in 2004 she received his ashes and began to process her feelings. Soon she felt called to write to veterans of any war, as well as those that love and care for them. Accepting the Ashes shares one family's story with hope that other veterans and their families might not have to wait 30 years before they heal their inner wounds caused by the traumas of military duty.

Accepting the Ashes expands on the following ideas to give guidance to those in pain right now.

1) Assume that anyone who has experienced combat has PTSD to some degree, whether they will admit it or not.

2) Partners and loved ones (especially women) cannot expect discussion about painful past experiences.

3) Many times, suffering people cannot express their pain and won't seek help, especially men.

4) When a soldier does not come home from battle, their children are most at risk.

5) Changing marriage partners or using medication won't erase grief.

6) How the veteran views their military service, as well as the cultural recognition of their service, affects how severe their PTSD may be and how they deal with it.

7) If you find your loved one wearing their uniform in inappropriate places, assume that they might not be at peace with their war experience.

8) Many will try to mask or numb pain.

9) When the vet does express a desire for physical or emotional help - HELP!

10) As soon as possible ask the returned vet "Are you resolved with what happened during your service?"

I also offer some navigation points as you move along the path of healing –

❖   There is a place for everyone.

❖   Change can happen.

❖   You have to say 'yes' to something, not just 'no' to something, to change behavior.

❖   War changes people. Period.

❖   You have to demand the right to heal.

Author's note about the word "Disorder"

When I wrote this book in 2004, Post Traumatic Stress was commonly referred to as a "Disorder". Today, more veterans, families, and mental health professionals are aware that physical, mental and emotional reactions to trauma are normal, not a "disorder", and are adjusting their therapies and language accordingly.

I use the phrase Post Traumatic Stress, and will include "Disorder" in this book, since it is still widely understood. However, I am pleased to see this change in our language, a change in the direction of healing.

A note about 2021, 20 years later...
This book is re-issued in September of 2021, to acknowledge the mark of 20 years after 9/11/2001 and honor the sacrifices of too many Americans in the last two decades who were sent to war in Iraq and Afghanistan.

I wrote this book a year after the invasion of Iraq because my experience with my father told me that a new generation of children, families and veterans would be wounded in ways that are often overlooked. 20+ years later, the healing is still needed, and the many traumas of war are still being passed to yet one more generation.

**Accepting the Ashes - A Daughter's Look
at Military Post Traumatic Stress Disorder**

By Quynn Elizabeth

My father died suddenly and unexpectedly in 2004,
and as I went through the few remaining boxes of of
his life, I realized that he had a story to be told, and
since he was not able to tell it, I decided I needed to.

He died at the age of 62, young by today's standards,
but his spirit was old from his life experience. In
1964, when he was 23, he enlisted in the Navy.
My father volunteered to go to Viet Nam, twice.

I am a combat veteran's daughter, and this story is about a veteran's experiences, mostly after he came home from his second tour.

My father's story is of interest now because we as a people have once again been in a 20 year war, and I feel I need to give voice to what often comes from it, the inner wounds of Post Traumatic Stress.

I am not a psychiatrist, but I am a daughter with over three decades of experience watching a man with a quiet, broken heart, and I am a woman who has the perspective of one who has just looked into the deepest recesses of her father's heart and mind, and there are some things that need to be said.

◆◆◆ Post Traumatic Stress is a condition of persistent mental and emotional stress occurring as a result of injury or severe psychological shock. Symptoms can include panic attacks, nightmares, insomnia, hyper-vigilance, flashbacks, outbursts of anger and irritability, concentration and attention problems and the inability to relax.

There are many ways in which a person can be left with symptoms of PTSD. War trauma is unique because in combat, stress is created by many experiences: the fear of death, the stress of not being able to trust the civilians around you, watching and hearing the terror of bloody death, seeing your friends and allies get hurt or die, the guilt of survival, regret, and finally the feelings associated with being ordered to kill others, even when the "others" are the "enemy".

Since the Viet Nam war, PTSD has become a term that many people are familiar with, but intellectually knowing that trauma is real does not alleviate the symptoms for those who experience them. Bessel van der Kolk, MD and Trauma Researcher, says in his book "The Body Keeps the Score" that trauma is specifically an experience that overwhelms the central nervous system, altering the way we process memories and how we live our lives.

"Trauma is not the story of something that happened back then, it's the current imprint of that pain, horror, and fear living inside people." Bessel van der Kolk

The best way forward as a culture and a world is that every soldier is offered all the help they need in coming to terms with combat trauma. If this does not come to pass, the pain continues, and it is passed on through who knows how many families for multiple generations.

I speak from my own multigenerational experience. The short version is this: My father volunteered to go to Viet Nam. He served as a Lieutenant Junior Grade. He lived through the first tour, and then signed up to go again, this time enlisting in Special Forces. In between tours he met my mother. The morning after my parents got engaged, he was called to the Navy counter insurgency school, then back to Viet Nam. A year later he came home, my parents immediately started a family, then my father attempted to put his warrior past behind him.

However, his past wouldn't leave him alone. While he told me a couple of years before he died, "I know now that I drink to numb my feelings", he drank alcohol more consistently and heavily over the years and became more emotionally distant from his growing family. Although I remember him as a kind man and a good father, fifteen years after his war experience he and my mother separated, splitting our family. After the painful divorce, the relationship between father and children was, in many ways, severed.

I reestablished intermittent contact ten years before he died as he was sliding down a slippery slope of alcoholism, which had led to him losing his career, and then his ability to drive. He was riddled with feelings of loneliness and tormenting guilt about not reaching out to his sons as he always told me he wanted to. When he could no longer pretend that his life wasn't in shambles, he began to admit and accept the role that his Viet Nam experience had played in his life.

DOWN AND OUT

Two years before his death I found my father alone in his apartment, looking horrible. This was by far the worst I had seen him. I could tell he was at the end of his proverbial rope and that he was deciding to live or die. I insisted on taking him to the VA's alcohol diversion program that very moment because he had just recently got his first ever DUI. Once there, I watched my father as he sat across from a grey haired veteran and substance abuse counselor. Immediately, this man began saying things to him like "I know how you feel, you can't sleep, and you feel guilty, right?" The dumbfounded look on my father's face said so much.

Thirty years after his war experience, and after a few alcohol diversion programs, he still felt that his problems were only his failings, that he was "weak" and just couldn't "handle it". Obvious to me, but an amazing revelation to him, he was not alone in how he felt. This humbling experience helped give my father the strength to get a second wind and in his last two difficult years, he was able to look at much of his past. The summer before he died, I spent five days camping with him. I was quietly shocked to hear him tell stories about Viet Nam, saying over and over, "I've never told this to anyone". I was grateful that he could finally speak them and that he felt he could say them to me.

As a strange gift, my father kept many papers relating to his life. While going through the boxes after his sudden death I found documentation of everything, his youth, his warrior phase, his family years, legal battles, and his fall into a deep well of emotional pain that he had been able to keep at bay as a younger man. Through reading these papers, I was able to step into his world which I had not known before. For years, I only saw him occasionally because alcohol and sadness had overtaken his ability to hold his life together and it was just too painful for me to watch. However, we were both given a chance to heal old wounds. Little did I know that it was a last chance before he died. I'm glad that I took the opportunity.

I would imagine that just about everyone has some unresolved issues with their father, veteran or not, so I am grateful to have watched my father in his older years, learning to understand how a phase in his young life fundamentally wounded him, and those around him, even though he didn't want to admit it. In his last few years, I got to know him as a man and I realized the burden he had carried alone, without really knowing that he was carrying something. While I feel resolved with my father, I feel an immense sadness about how things turned out.

I wonder, what if things were different, what if the culture supported, even insisted on, my father's healing, and all the others like him?
So many what ifs...

IT WILL BE ALRIGHT WHEN...
So now he is gone, but there are many more men, and now women, like him who were in a far away land telling themselves that everything will be alright when they get home. Once home, they have done the best they could to get on with life. But what happens when the regret and memories don't go away? What then? What about the spouses, parents and children who don't know what to do with the intense feelings being displayed? How do we all deal with our loved ones when they have to come to terms with what they did, including actively killing other human beings, or didn't do, by leaving them behind? This is why I write to you, my father is one

version of the future of your soldier, your loved one, your neighbor or client, or YOU, 30 years from now. I have some pieces of advice, some ideas that have come from my experience, and I offer them to you, to anyone, who might find them to be helpful.

Your soldier is my parent.

I am your daughter.

We are all in this together.

PIECES OF THE PUZZLE

It is important to say that each person is unique, based on their personality, circumstance and support system. Every veteran's experience is as individual as they are, so there are no rules, per se, but if we look for the answers not within a book of rules, but from within the truth of each person, and we assume that painful feelings want to be resolved, that human beings want to be at peace, we can find an answer that fits for each individual and that helps society as a whole.

There are some humans who are comfortable with being professional soldiers, let's call them 'career warriors'. I'm talking here about term soldiers, ones who experience a phase of warriorship, and then re-enter civilian society and attempt to rejoin their lives.

It is also important to mention that today, in contrast to Viet Nam, the United States does not have a draft (at least at this writing). To take a quick look at our military forces, as stated earlier, some joined the military because it was their life dream to be a soldier, some became soldiers as a response to the attacks on September 11, 2001, and other men and women joined the military out of loyalty to the

United States or to enhance their personal life (education, benefits, travel, etc.).

While each soldier is a great patriot for answering the call of duty, some did not sign up specifically to fight in a war, any war. Whichever camp you or your loved one belongs to, please accept the following concepts as ideas to help your family assess any pain that remains from the war experience, now or in the future. For those of you whose loved ones have not yet returned, consider yourself recruited as chief sentry and support coordinators for years to come. They will need it.

Finally, let's agree that the military is a male dominated environment. This discussion affects and refers to women, as well as men, but since women service members are trained in a male oriented system, I will use the pronoun 'he', but also sometimes "they/them". If you are a female soldier, I'm talking about you as well.

"Often I experienced constant shelling from mortars, artillery and sniper fire. The screaming of the wounded and terrified, the sickly sweet smell of morphine and the sight of a base watch dog bringing a human femur to the medical bunker as a retriever dog would do, will be with me forever." Quote from

my father's VA PTSD assessment questionnaire- 30 years after Viet Nam

While there are a thousand things that could be helpful to a veteran and his family, I have consolidated my experience into ten ideas to think about when dealing with potential PTSD symptoms. After those, I list five guidance points to keep in mind as one moves toward healing.

1) **It is safe to assume that anyone who has experienced combat has PTSD to some degree, whether they would admit it or not.**

The negative effects of PTSD depend on a person's personality, life circumstances and how much support they have. Anyone who is close to a veteran must be prepared to deal with second hand PTSD, meaning you will experience aspects of what your loved one is experiencing, whether they openly speak of it or not.

Understand that if you partner with or marry a combat veteran, either before or after combat occurs, you are enlisting in a psychological challenge, so pay attention! Whether you marry/partner with a soldier, then he goes to combat and comes home to you (physically wounded or not), or if you meet and marry him after he returns from his tour of duty, remember that even though the soldier wants to get on with his life, once he is home, his war experience is NOT over.

If you are wondering if someone has PTSD, pay attention and watch for talk and behavior that are indicators. In addition to the symptoms listed here, look for signs of depression, anger, being emotionally reclusive and non-communicative. To be honest, many men exhibit these symptoms even if they haven't been in combat, so you must assess this for yourself.

My father, when he finally decided that he did exhibit signs of PTSD, received a 10% post-trauma disability from the government. At the time he died, he was receiving 50%. This is an example of the difficulty of judging how much of a person's behavior is due to PTSD and how much is due to other reasons.

One issue that may surprise you is that when your veteran returns, he may feel that aspects of civilian life are boring. For those in the generation of war video gamers and folks looking for adrenaline rushes, we have to realize that, while it may sound strange to civilians, war combat may seem to be the ultimate extreme experience. In addition to patriotism, the quest for "adventure" and "exhilaration" are reasons why many originally volunteer for the military. However, few soldiers are prepared for the emotional stress created when one survives a battle, or has to kill.

An article called "Trained to Kill, Not to Cope" by Charles Duhigg describes how the military admittedly offers no training in emotionally handling battle and killing.

"The idea and experience of killing another person is not addressed in military training. Training's intent is to re-create battle, to make it an automatic

behavior among soldiers" Col. Thomas Burke- Past Director of mental health policy for the Defense Dept.

The reason my father signed up for a second tour of duty was because he lived through, to use his word, an "exhilarating" firefight towards the end of his first tour. The emotional rush that he felt as a young soldier was so great that he volunteered to go to Viet Nam again, this time in Special Forces. Little did he know how these experiences would linger with him as an older man, back in "the world".

2) Partners and loved ones (especially women) cannot expect discussion about painful past experiences.

I have heard many wives, partners and girlfriends say that they have asked their loved one about their war experiences and received an answer like "How would you know what I feel?" "Only a handful could understand and they are dead" "I don't want to talk about it." or "You don't need to hear about that". We all must understand that male culture does not encourage discussion about emotional pain, period, so why should we expect our men to talk openly about things that are, to them (or you), vile and horrifying?

Whether their silence comes from a desire to protect their loved ones from unpleasantness, their own feelings of shame, or their desire for a mental block, each veteran needs to find a way to come to terms with his own feelings. If he cannot talk to loved ones, he still needs to talk to someone, ideally a person who can understand and is capable of dealing with this kind of pain in a way that promotes healing for our vets, because an unhealed veteran is everyone's problem.

Growing up, I have no memories of my father speaking of his war experiences. Honestly, looking back, because he was in the Navy and I didn't know any better, I thought he simply sailed around the ocean in a ship when he was in the military. It was only when I was 18 years old and went to see the movie Platoon did I began to understand and wonder what my father might have gone through.

My mother shared her experience that during their seventeen year marriage, he never talked about "it". Can you imagine, never talking about such a formidable experience with the person closest to you? There was one time, within a few years of his return to civilian life, when my father woke up out of sleep, screaming that he had killed someone. The next morning he denied that he said it.

It's amazing to me now, looking back, that the one thing that affected my father so deeply and that caused so many devastating problems for three decades in my family, was never discussed. Alcoholism always got the blame, and it was alcohol that caused so many pains, but the underlying issue was why my father drank. It was the family secret, apparently even to him.

Finally, my father did talk to me. As I mentioned earlier, the summer before he died, he sat with me around a campfire, telling stories I had never heard before. After each confession he said "I've never told this to anyone." Even though he may have spoken of these things before, I felt that something important was happening because he was confessing to me, his first child and only daughter.

"The more soldiers ignore their emotions and behave like trained machines rather than thinking people, the more you invite PTSD." - Dr. David Spiegel-Stanford University School of Medicine

Something to remember is that most of us have experienced trauma at various ages in our lives, so a veteran's traumatic experiences during military service may not be their only ones. The effects of childhood trauma (including Complex PTSD*) are

real and also needs tending. PTSD is generally
related to a single event or series of events within a
short period of time, while *Complex PTSD is related
to a series of events that repeatedly occurred over
an extended period of time (often during childhood).
Often childhood trauma can be re-activated in
stressful situations during military service.

3) Many times, suffering people cannot express their pain and won't seek help, especially men.

I admit that this is a gross overgeneralization, but it needs to be said anyway. Men are not often encouraged to outwardly express their feelings, especially sadness, confusion, regret, shame, fear, frustration and pain.

I have heard men say they worry that expressing such emotions admits weakness and leaves them open to vulnerability, possibly even violence from other men. Our culture teaches boys this and the military intensifies it, so when soldiers find themselves unsure or in pain, many may feel overwhelmed by their feelings. I believe that we need to admit this cultural norm to understand why men might not want to seek help when it is truly needed.

My father said that when he was discharged from the Navy, he wanted out so badly that he didn't want to call attention to any potential problem or even ask a question. "Yes, sir, No, sir, get me out of here" was his attitude. It was over 20 years after his war experience, when he was not a young man anymore, that he admitted that he might have some problems, both physical and emotional.

He began to admit to himself that his hearing was severely damaged and while he did not admit it earlier in life, he knew it was from being exposed to loud explosions while in the Navy. In 1991 he petitioned for a hearing loss disability to pay for hearing aids, which he couldn't afford, and was denied.

Apparently, since my father had never said anything before, the government officials did not believe that the hearing loss was related to his soldier experience so long ago.

I knew that my father always had trouble hearing, but while growing up, I thought it was just who he was. I remember feeling irritated by having to constantly repeat myself. "Pardon?" he would ask over and over. When he finally admitted to himself that he couldn't hear the phone ring and he bought one of those phones that light up when it rings, I realized that I needed to help him get help. He set up another meeting to appeal the earlier VA decision and I went with him. At the end of that meeting he told them that he had resisted asking for help from the military for years, but he'd decided that since he had served his country, it was ok to ask for help. The commission tested his hearing and found that he had over 50% hearing loss and approved his application.

In his later years my father got help from the VA in the form of alcohol treatment, vocational training, hearing aids and Post Traumatic Stress Disorder counseling, but because of his self-described pride, he experienced decades of resisting the idea that anything was wrong with him and any problem brought to his attention was ultimately someone's else's. I share these personal stories because there are many, many others out there just like my father and I feel for all the children who don't, and won't for a long time, understand why their loved one, and family, is experiencing pain, yet won't admit it.

Many who are in pain yet don't acknowledge it try to hide their feelings from the public world so they can say "See, everything is ok". So your loved one may hide behind alcohol or another pain medication or put up a mental block and want to continue in the everyday world. "The past is the past" they may say, but pain doesn't just go away. It must be dealt with. PTSD is hidden from public view, but is most apparent in the veterans' closest emotional relationships.

Unfortunately, there are times when veterans' emotional distress is brought into the public sphere. My father ended his career when he came to meetings drunk and said 'inappropriate' things to workmates. He was asked to submit his resignation. Sometimes, public displays can be dangerous to self and other. We all pray for peaceful outcomes in those unfortunate situations, and help for those who need it.

For everyone's safety= spouses and partners, it is important to be aware of warning signs within your loved one and yourself. Remember, if you are with someone who has combat or a traumatic military experience, you have enlisted in dealing with PTSD as well. When a member of your household wakes up screaming in the middle of the night, you and your family are up with them. If a returned veteran becomes moody or irritable at home, their child may become angry or irritated at school, leading to a cycle of discipline or possibly medication or worse. Trauma in the home affects all involved.

I have learned that healing is a difficult, painful, vulnerable, and tiring endeavor, but it is absolutely worth the effort. It is not easy to heal oneself and one's family, but it is the most important thing we can do. As a culture, we understand that it takes time and care to heal a physical wound. Now we, as a culture, need to learn and accept that inner wounds from trauma are just as real.

4) **When a soldier does not come home from battle, their children are most at risk for PTSD.**

My father enlisted for a second tour in Viet Nam because he lived through an "exhilarating" fire fight the first time he was there. To many, that may seem like a strange reason to re-enlist, but the reason that meant so much to him was because his father was a bomber pilot in WWII, shot down over the Pacific when my father was a toddler. He grew up hearing hero stories about his pilot father, and how he was bravely killed in battle. I remember my dad telling me that only years after his combat experiences did he realize he would actually stand up in firefights, somehow trying to die like his father, the hero.

While going through my father's things after his death, I found an old newspaper article in his mother's Bible. It was written around 1944, within the year after my father lost his dad. Apparently, a local newspaper man met my grandmother and was impressed by her story. I would like to share it because the way she felt after losing her husband to war is how many loved ones feel right now about their loss.

THERE IS ALWAYS THE FUTURE
(No author listed)

This writer has met a real heroine. Her husband not long ago met death while fighting the enemies of his country. He had not long been gone from home. When he left his last embraces were for his young wife and their small son (my father).

The widow says *"At our home, we do not cry. I always feel like crying, and sometimes, even when I am downtown I catch myself on the point of breaking down. Then I tell myself I must be brave. If I did give way it would set a bad example-a bad example for myself, for my little boy who is just like his daddy and those who are at home. Then too, there are other women who had a loss like mine. I know they suffer as I do. And they do not let themselves break down. "There is nothing any of us can do about it. If my husband had to go, death came as he would have had it come, while he was fighting the enemy he was sent out to fight. At home, we laugh, joke and tease*

each other, as we used to do. It is very hard, though,
to appear gay when our hearts are so sad.

"My job now is to try and help our parents to get
over the shock and to raise my little boy to be as near
as possible as his father would want him to be. The
baby remembers his father and some things he said
just before he left us the last time. I am trying to
keep alive in the baby's memory everything I can
about his father- and to keep my own chin up."

In addition to the newspaper clipping, I found an old
photograph of my dad, maybe four or five years old,
in a small military uniform, saluting for the
camera. The caption explained that the outfit he
wore was made from one of his dead father's
uniforms. He never spoke of this to me while he was
alive, yet I know it impacted him on many levels.

Losing a loved one to war is the ultimate loss and the effects of that loss are felt for generations. Of course, for any of you who have suffered such a loss, my heart goes out to you and I understand that I cannot know what you are feeling. Children whose parent doesn't come home have it especially hard because, in addition to the loss that they feel, their parent becomes a mythical hero, and there is no input into the hero myth by the vet himself. A one-sided hero myth is hard to live up to, at least my father found it to be so. I think he felt guilty for living through his war experience, since he was brought up by his southern mother to be "just like his daddy".

Children are at risk, even when their loved one does come home, because children are not able to logically understand why their parent is hurting or "different" or wounded. As already mentioned, there are many things that are not spoken when a soldier returns home. Most veterans would never burden their children with horrifying or troubling experiences and so nothing unpleasant is said, but understand that children pick up on everything even if they do not understand. If your relationship is stressed, your children pick up on it. If you end up parting ways, your children will be affected. Knowing how children are delicate and resilient, adults need to be especially sensitive to children's emotional reactions to our adult, and sometimes painful, world.

5)Changing marriage partners or using medication won't erase grief.

No matter how great the desire to make the pain go away, masking the pain just doesn't work in the long run. People start relationships for many reasons, and people in pain will do almost anything to not be in pain, so I can understand the desire to move on and make a new start, but if, after using medication (prescribed or self-medication) or after the second or third marriage, you find your problems and pain are still with you, seek help. It's nothing to be ashamed of.

"Killing unleashes emotions few people are prepared to deal with. We help soldiers put those emotions and experiences away, so they can go into battle the next day." Capt. Robert Cardona, a psychiatrist with a combat stress-control team based in Southern Iraq

6) How the veteran views their military service to society, compared to cultural recognition of their service, affects how severe their PTSD may be and how they deal with it.

Since the dawn of human existence, groups of people have found reasons to go to war with each other. Whether war is inherent in humanity, I don't know, but tribes, villages and nations have always participated in the activity, to prove bravery of warriors, right perceived wrongs and establish territory. So the question is not whether war as a concept is "ok", but rather if a particular war is seen by the participating culture as justified and honorable. My opinion is that when certain actions, including killing a person or group, are seen as necessary to the warrior and his society, tribe or family, their emotional response might be quite different than if the reason for killing is not seen as acceptable to the person who is asked to do it.

We, as individuals might not like to think about killing that way, but I would argue that it is true. However, whether or not it is true is not the point, the point is how your soldier, as an individual, feels about their war experience and how this coincides with how their society views the same war.

First, let's agree that exploding bombs, screams of terror and being surrounded by death, causes trauma no matter how the vet feels about the war in which they fought. It is important, however, to understand how your veteran feels about being sent to this particular war, (whichever one it might be), as well as the details about how the war was/is being fought.

My father volunteered to go to Viet Nam, however one of the commendation awards he received was for a horrifying experience when, as a boat officer for a SEAL/Marine amphibious landing, three out of four of his crew members were killed in front of him by enemy fire. Besides the guilt and pain that he carried for the deaths, he also was angry.

"I was filled with guilt and frustration and rage that my men were exposed to a high degree of danger with such an appalling lack of planning." (Quote taken from his Veteran's Administration post-traumatic stress disorder questionnaire-1994)

When he expressed his frustration to his commanding officers, he was basically told to shut up and do his job. I only found out about this from reading letters that he wrote before his death. Apparently, being told that he didn't know enough to have an opinion negatively affected him all of his life.

To bring this into current times~ For veterans who served in Iraq, Afghanistan, or any future war, whether a soldier agrees with the premise and execution of these wars (including the withdrawal of forces) does matter to their wellbeing.

Now these specific traumas are called "Moral Injury", a term coined by Psychiatrist Jonathan Shay or "Soul Injury", a term coined by Deborah Grassman of Opus Peace. Both describe the lasting effects of the betrayal, grief and shame that results when a service member (in theater or remote combat) perpetrates, witnesses, or fails to prevent acts that transgress one's morals.

When someone is asked to fight for a cause, one hopefully supports the cause and respects how it is handled. If not, expect that the veteran will have to go to great lengths, extra lengths, to come to terms with what they did in service to their country.

WHEN THEY COME HOME HURT

In 2021 it is estimated that over 53,000 U.S. service members have been physically wounded in theater. While the military treats each wounded soldier with the latest technology in order to repair their body after damage has been done, the same level of care may not be as easily available once a soldier comes home.

We don't know how many veterans suffer from inner wounds related to their service. What happens if they don't get the continued care that they need, when they need it? It is to everyone's advantage to help those soldiers who have sacrificed receive all the assistance they require to heal their wounds so they can reintegrate into society without residual anger and resentment towards the very society for which they fought.

In addition to a physical wound, a veteran may have residual feelings about the wounding experience, or about surviving it. As a loved one, the most important thing you can do for your wounded veteran is to assess the situation as to what the vet needs, and don't be afraid if they let out uncomfortable or disturbing feelings about their situation. People tend to respond differently to pain and stress. While some might vent externally by expressing anger towards others, government officials or themselves, others may internalize their emotions, showing signs of depression, sadness or self-numbing behavior. It is also completely possible that one person will express themselves in many ways.

Healing from war trauma is the most difficult thing they (and you) may ever deal with. If you see symptoms of PTSD in addition to their physical wounds, help them contact a mental health care professional, immediately, and know you will need to be persistent.

7) If you find your loved one wearing their uniform in places that seem out of context, or if they desire to wear the uniform for days at a time, assume that they might not be at peace with their war experience.

As I went through my father's photographs, I was shocked to find images of him in his military uniform at various company costume parties. The most striking photo was one of him in his green uniform, with what I would hope was a pretend rifle in hand, crouching behind a desk in an office, smiling for the camera. While it may have seemed funny, or a little odd at the time, in context of knowing the extent of his PTSD, it is more disturbing than funny. If questioned about this kind of behavior, a vet might say "I want to wear this, or do this, or feel this way!" (I know my dad would have resisted that there was anything "wrong" with him at the time.)

I honor the fact that coping with PTSD is a dramatic undertaking, and there is no "right" way to do it, yet there is a difference between free will ("I WANT to do this!") and trying to cope with an intense emotional experience, so if you feel you or your loved one needs help, connect with a qualified counselor or helpful peer group.

"The military could train soldiers to talk about killing as easily as they train them to pull the trigger. But commanders are in denial. Nobody wants to accept the blame for a soldier who comes home a wreck for doing what his country asked him to do" - Lt. Col. Dave Grossman, retired psychology instructor at West Point

8) Many will try to mask or numb pain.

Without judgment, let me say that PTSD symptoms can increase with alcohol, substance or medication abstinence. In no way do I condone substance dependence, however, if and when a vet stops using a substance that acts as a numbing agent, and they suddenly have painful experiences, their incentive to continue their abstinence goes away. The emotional/physical pain might be stronger than the desire to be free from the substance. Also, whether they seek out a doctor's prescription of one mood altering drug or another, or they decide to self-medicate with alcohol, Cannabis, over the counter sleep aids or something else, understand that the specific desire to ward off nightmares is strong, considering that nightmarishly sleep-deprived nights are common for those who suffer from trauma.

While I understand that my father's addiction was a major factor in my painful family experiences, I realize now that it must have been difficult to be in the position to want to enjoy life, yet to have such painful emotions and to honestly not know what to do with them except to try to make them go away. As I wrote earlier, my father became self-aware enough in his older years to say "I know that I drink to numb my feelings". He did quit, a few times, yet he always seemed to reunite with his most consistent companion, alcohol. In my father's papers I found a Veteran's Administration assessment form quoting him in saying that his PTSD symptoms did increase during those times when he abstained. He also described his 30 year old nightmares, which were usually the same. He would regularly wake up from dreaming about a "VC" in black pajamas who tried to slit his throat while he slept.

Please remember that all medications, whether legal or illicit, are many times used to numb, mask and suppress painful feelings. However, they never really do, because the repressed emotions come out

one way or another, as anger, depression, suicide...
As chief sentry and care-giver, watch for moments
when your vet is dealing with a powerful emotional
feeling. Please don't run from these feelings and
don't help them suppress emotions.

Responding in ways like "Don't worry so much" or
"The past is the past" or "Don't talk about things like
that" can increase their desire to repress
emotions. The way that your veteran will come to
terms with their experiences, doubts and pains is to
express them so, don't be surprised when they do.
When and if they stop using, their feelings will
emerge and they will need to deal with them in a
safe and purposeful manner.

Also, be aware that PTSD symptoms increase or
recur with triggers. A trigger can be an unexpected
experience that reminds the veteran of a combat or
traumatizing situation. One thing I do remember
from childhood was that some movies upset my
father enough that he had to leave the
theater. Also, fireworks and loud noises startled him
all his life.   Veterans of urban wars are likely to be
triggered in cars, riding or driving in traffic, or worse,
gridlock.

Another war can set off memories as well. I found a letter dated September 16, 2001. In it my father expressed his concern that the United States would respond to the attacks in a way that would lead us down a long road similar to the Viet Nam war. He became much more troubled as the war in Iraq began and escalated. While his death was an accident (he fell and hit his head and died alone in his apartment) I am convinced that his mental anguish about the war was a contributing factor in the events that lead to him falling to his death. If he were alive in August of 2021, he would be extremely distraught by the unnecessary tragedies of the withdrawal of American troops and Afghan allies out of Afghanistan.

"Being close to death warps a person's mind." - Quote from my father's VA PTSD assessment - 1994

9) When the vet does express or display a desire for physical or emotional help - HELP!

We must be realistic and admit that the military establishment focuses on soldiers doing their jobs. Helping those same soldiers deal with the aftermath of doing those jobs is apparently not their priority. That could change, if we make it so, but until that happens we have to work within the system that is available to us. This being the case, when your loved one expresses a need, the best thing to do is to help him find out how he can receive the help he needs. Yet, remember that simply sending the vet to a program or to the "authorities" is not necessarily all it will take for him to heal. He has a much better chance if he has a support network, a community that can listen and accept him and his pains.

A CRY FOR HELP

Sometime in 1991, when I was 23 years old, I remember my father calling me at work upset that he had not been able to find a job after he resigned/was fired from his last one. Right there, on the phone, I told him that the reason he wasn't finding a job in the field he desired was because he looked like a drunk. I didn't say this to be mean, but I was frustrated with his lack of self-awareness in that moment. Needless to say, he didn't take my comment very well. We hung up. A while later, he called me back and told me that he had almost just shot himself in the head, but decided to call me instead. He asked me if I would take him to the local Veteran's Administration alcohol recovery program. I agreed. After he completed the program, he wrote in a questionnaire evaluating his PTSD that the program helped him "refocus my energies on positive things, and my attitude about how I relate to the world."

"We have to give soldiers a vocabulary to talk through emotions and teach them not to be embarrassed by troubling feelings." - Lt. Col. Dave Grossman

HOW YOU CAN HELP

-If you are a caregiver, and/or a loved one, listen to your vet. Division psychologist Capt. Mary Dorritie of Camp Casey in South Korea has had many soldiers rotate there from combat theaters in Iraq and Afghanistan. She has found that among the soldiers with PTSD, one of the most common complaints is not having people to talk about it with. (Seth Robson, Stars and Stripes 6/15/04)

-Take matters into your own hands! Find a book, ask questions and read websites to familiarize yourself with symptoms and common experiences.

-Take into consideration special circumstances such as sexual assault and systemic racism that can add layers to the trauma and can make it harder to seek help.

-Do not ignore the problems, and don't encourage the vet to ignore them either. Instead, assume that this is something that can be helped, managed, and possibly even treated over time. The veteran may feel overwhelmed by the problem and not know what to do. Remember that for their entire military experience, soldiers have been told to "Buck up!" "Get over it!" and "Be a man/warrior!" There may be reluctance on the part of a veteran to go against this ingrained advice and share their feelings. He may feel that there will be negative repercussions because of his request for help. Whether or not this happens, stand by them however you can.

Always, the best way you can help is to be a supportive witness to your loved one's pain because pain is nothing to be ashamed of, even for tough and brave soldiers.

THE UNSPEAKABLE
A horrifying part of war is that it sets the stage for soldiers to commit unspeakable acts. What happens to a soldier's mind when he participates in killing

civilians? How does one feel when he accidentally, or purposefully, kills women or children? Or cannot stop the murders of others? Where do these actions fit into the idea of a just and honorable war? These moments stay with a veteran forever and are exceptionally difficult to deal with. So, as a loved one, especially if you are a woman, be aware that there may be parts of your veteran's experience that they are particularly reluctant to think about, let alone speak about them.

A MESSAGE TO FATHERS, GRANDFATHERS, MENTORS AND FRIENDS

If you are a man in heterosexual culture, whether you are in the military or not, it is understood that you, and 90% of all the men you know, are very careful not to act "feminine", at least around other men.

It is important to tell you brothers, for your sons and grandsons and friends that are veterans, the best thing you can do for them and yourself, is to be brave enough to feel what you both feel. If that means either of you feel the need to cry, CRY. Your veteran may feel confused. He may feel angry or sad without knowing how to deal with his feelings. He has probably been told by his military leaders to "suck it up" and "don't be a pussy!" (I apologize for using foul language, however, I do believe that this is a word heard often in the military.) So, if a veteran's male loved ones can show him that to cry, if his heart wants to, is to be a strong man, it will help him heal.

War is an incredibly sad experience. Young male soldiers need emotionally expressive older men to show them the way, so be willing to cry together, cry in front of him, let him cry in front of you without stopping the experience out of embarrassment. It may feel difficult, but crying is the body's physical outlet for emotional grief for men as well as women. If that outlet is denied because of an inappropriate cultural belief, everyone loses.

10) As soon as possible ask the returned vet "Are you resolved with what happened?"

Since every human being is different, the only way to get an idea about how someone feels about something, is to ask. It is appropriate and desirable to begin dialog and discussion as soon as possible after a soldier's return. The tendency may be to not want to talk about difficult things, but my experience tells me that once silence has begun, it is much more difficult down the road to implement an open dialog. So, find the right time and ask your vet how they feel about their military experiences.

Why ask this? This question will offer the vet, as well as the questioner, an opportunity to think about how they feel about their situation. If when asked, your vet reacts angrily, that tells you something even though he didn't tell you anything specific. If he starts to cry, that tells you something. If he thoughtfully tells you how he feels, then you know how he feels in that moment. Worries about money, family and being back in society are stressful parts of a returning vet's experience. They may need help in a number of ways. Asking this question offers an opportunity to find out about where one hurts, both physically and emotionally.

As a questioner, if your vet's answer overwhelms you, or makes you feel like shutting down, that tells you something about your ability to take in uncomfortable information. While our culture may teach otherwise, talking about feelings is never a bad thing. It may be uncomfortable, but feeling unresolved is worse. It is important for vets to know that whatever they feel is the way they feel. It is not wrong or permanent. If they are afraid, ok. If they are sad or confused, ok. It in no way means that they are less of a warrior or that they are weak. They have gone through a traumatic experience. Humans are feeling beings, trauma makes people feel many things. Everyone can heal with some help.

◆ ◆ ◆

I would like to share five things that I have learned
by watching and working with my father, and seeing
how his experiences affected my family.

**1) There is a place for everyone.
No one is so unworthy as to not have a place.**

I listed this concept first of the following five
because I think it is so important, yet I found myself
writing all other sections first, leaving this one to the
last. Somehow it is the most difficult to explain, and

in a way, the most important. As so often happens, one (including me) can easily avoid that which is most painful. So, why is this one so difficult? This concept includes folks trying to love and have families. What happens, honestly, if it doesn't work out?

In war, people do things that they might never do in "real life". Many who come home are filled with guilt and shame about their experiences, about what they did, or maybe what they didn't do. When service members become "veterans", they often want to put all that behind them, find love, or come back to their love, and move on. But love is a strange thing. In order to love, one must open their heart to another person. This is very difficult to do if there are things in one's heart that one does not want revealed.

The human ability to couple and get together lustfully, and lovingly, is great, but that phase always transforms into everyday love. While the non-veteran may remain open hearted toward their partner after the honeymoon period, the vet may suddenly, or slowly, seem incapable of remaining open, which can lead to feelings of anger or bewilderment on the part of their partner and more guilt or shame for the veteran. In addition to any issues of PTSD in the marriage mix, we live in a culture where 50% of married couples divorce. Marriage is a gamble no matter with whom you try it, PTSD or not.

So what if doesn't work out? Who is to blame? Whose fault is it that the person who once seemed open and loving is now closed and distant? This is a difficult issue to talk about because people, veterans and non-veterans, get married for many reasons and many times it just doesn't work out. I have no answers to this dilemma, I only have a few suggestions from my own family experience to keep in mind, for those partners and children who can't understand why it is the way it is.

For all of you who are children of service members, or adult children of veterans of past wars: if your parents divorce(d), or if your veteran leaves your family, understand this. Your veteran acts towards you as he feels about himself. Don't automatically assume that you are the problem, or unwanted, or somehow flawed. Whether your father admits it or not, if he went through a war, his heart is sad. If his marriage did not work out with your mother, he feels like a failure. He is embarrassed that it didn't succeed and honestly, you may remind him of his failure. He may have even remarried and now has a "new family". My advice is, do not take it personally. Hard to do, I know, but try, because believe me, it is not YOU. Try reaching out to him, be willing to be honest with him, don't be afraid to tell him how you feel, and be open to hearing how he feels. Yet don't take it personally if he can't, or won't, open to you. It is not your fault. While there is never an excuse for abusive behavior, sometimes knowing why someone acts the way they do can help you heal.

One does not have to die to be a causality of war. I call this section "There is a place for everyone" because after surviving combat one or one hundred times, a veteran's place may not be with his family. Being in a healthy family requires an open heartedness and that may be too painful for some. My father was a good father, yet as the years went on, he became more and more emotionally distant from those with whom he lived. What was going on in his head, I do not know, because he wouldn't talk much about anything.

Finally, after tiring of living in an alcoholic marriage, my mother asked for a separation from my father when I was in my early teens. As each year passed after the divorce, his relationship with his children dwindled more and more until it got to that horrible place of him wanting to call, yet he felt guilty for not doing what he should have done in the past, and so, once again, he didn't call. The saddest thing to me is that, because it didn't work out between my father and my mother, my father ignorantly sacrificed the potential of his relationship with his three sons. As I watched my dad cry about this many times in his last years, yet still not call, I realized that regret is a torturing emotion.

So many men, whether they ever set foot in the military, seem to have difficulty in this area of life but my focus here is on those men who have an extra monkey on their backs, which is PTSD, a devastating syndrome that can eat away at the most tender hearted person, and contribute to them feeling like a failure in the sacred domain of parenthood and love. Every civilian partner needs to look at their loved one honestly, their strengths as well as their challenges. If you are with a veteran, assume that on one level or another your lover has a broken heart, because war is heartbreaking. You, and the love you bring to them, may be able to heal their heart sadness, and it may not.

Of course, it is absolutely possible to partner with a veteran in a loving and open relationship. Love can heal many wounds. However, if, for whatever reason, your paths do diverge, the optimum scenario is that each person involved is supported in their healing and quest to find their place. I know it is difficult to be civil when one is hurting, but no matter how disappointed or frustrated you are by your partnership experience, remember that no one is so unworthy as to not have a place. If the veteran's place ends up not being with you, and you have children together, try not to speak of deficiencies of the vet as a person in front of or to the children. This bad habit only causes more problems for everyone involved.

Children do not understand the intricacies of adult relationships so if they grow up hearing only your perspective, as a partner or lover, about their veteran father, it will color their perceptions about him as a man which they should be able to create for themselves over time. Also, if the father knows how you speak of him to his children, it affects his self-esteem which makes it more likely that he will resist participating in his children's lives or cooperating with you. Strange, I know, but unfortunately often times it is true.

Divorce is painful and difficult. If you have to go through this harrowing experience and you find yourself disappointed, angry or frustrated with your partner, spare your children the adult details, even if they are teenagers. Instead, talk to another adult. Remember that what your children experience in your love, as well as divorce, will affect their lives and their own path to love for a very long time.

2) Change CAN happen.

After my father's death I not only received many of his belongings, I also inherited his ashes. The reason my father didn't die a more depressing death than he did was because he made the choice to live and then he became open to the idea that his life could change. He cleared his head in yet another alcohol diversion program and gained new skills in a VA assisted job retraining course. Then he found something to hold on to, a new project that helped him see something positive in the world.

In my father's younger years, he worked to build a career until his personal life overtook him and by his late 50s he could not hold a job.   For the last two years of his life, my father worked on an idea of how he would spend his 'old age'. His plan was that when he began receiving his social security (a year away at that point) he would travel around the northwestern United States, collecting information and experiences regarding his favorite interests. As my dad would say in his later life "old dogs CAN learn new tricks."

He was supposed to travel during the summer of 2004. However, he died in March of that year. I guess the point was not for my father to physically travel, the point, for him, was that he wanted to do it, and his inspiration inspired me to travel in his intended footsteps that summer, to write this book, to enhance my own healing and to train as a Soul Restoration Practitioner to be able to help others heal their inner wounds.

3) You have to say 'yes' to something, not just 'no' to something, to change behavior.

My experience has taught me, both in dealing with my father's healing, as well as my own, that in order to move beyond a sad or painful time in one's life, one needs something positive to move towards. Whether it is a way to share one's experience with others, being of service, or to immerse one's self in a positive project, in order to truly heal, a person needs to fill the empty hole of pain with something life affirming, something that can help heal the old wound a little bit each day. Honestly, for some the goal may be to feel a little bit better, most days.

4) War changes people. Period.

As relatives and loved ones of veterans, we must understand that the "normal" of before their war experience simply doesn't exist afterwards. A new "normal" needs to be created. This can be said in a short sentence, yet it takes a lifetime to create. If you ever need an affirmation or mantra in the difficult times to help you understand what in the world is going on, remind yourself "War changes people. Period."

5) Demand the right to heal.

Each individual and family in every culture deserves the right to heal the wounds of war, whether they have access to the tools to do so, or not. Since everyone who participates in war, no matter how they personally feel about it, is affected, helping our soldiers, who are also our fathers, sons, daughters, lovers and friends, heal their bodies, hearts and minds, is a necessity, not a privilege.

Most soldiers do not have the ability to deal with the emotions they are experiencing while doing their tour of duty, so the attention must begin once they come home. This makes healing a group effort. My advice? Be bold, be persistent, be the squeaky wheel. Do whatever it takes to get some help and do not feel ashamed for asking. Demand the right to heal the wounds caused by the machine of war. If we do not? My father was diagnosed with chronic, moderate PTSD. I pray for all the men and women diagnosed, or more importantly, undiagnosed, with severe symptoms. They are our problem and responsibility as well. People of any nation traumatized by war are more likely to recreate their trauma, by recreating war over and over, generation after generation. If not healed, this painful legacy will be felt for many more generations to come.

As I said in the beginning, a person's ability to heal the past is affected by a number of things including the personality of the veteran, their life circumstances and the level of support that they have. How is it that my father reacted to life by drinking alcohol and crumbling before my eyes when it seems that other veterans with even more horrific experiences have lived peaceful lives with seemingly no regrets? I don't know. Is it fate? Karma? Luck? Yes and no. In the healing formula of personality, circumstance and support, I know now that my father did not have a strong support network to help him deal with the feelings he had. I am also aware that my father had a personality that he himself described as prideful, especially as a young man.

The following quote is from the transcript of the hearing in 1994 when my father petitioned the VA for hearing aids. He was describing why it took him so long to ask for help.

"I took an over amount of pride in my own self-reliance, I would not admit that I had any problems. Looking back, I should have done things differently. I realize that now, but it has taken me a long time to get to the point of understanding what I should have done. It has taken me a long time to grow up."

The desire to understand the past is a strong one, and sometimes a futile one. I hope that we, as a culture, can increase our learning curve so that another generation doesn't have to spend the next 30 years coming to terms with what has happened to their families. Will they have to spend decades healing their hearts and mourning their physically and emotionally broken parents as I did? Only time will answer that question.

I will leave the final words to my father, a quote that I found after his death as he was coming to terms with the (then new) war and how he felt about it, as a veteran of another war, three decades before. 20 years+ later, it is still true.

"As an officer in the Navy, I raised questions about the war 35 years ago and was told "Shut up and do your job! You don't have the big picture!". I had a big picture then, and now at age 60, I have a mural in mind that includes answers to the questions in my heart. I finally know that while the government may not want to listen, what I think is right for me."

My prayers are with you, your loved ones, and all who are ready to tend the inner wounds of life, including war.

This project has been an act of love and resolution:

-Thanks to my mother, for taking care of the details of my father's death, for supporting me in telling this story and helping me to heal over time. I know it was tough for her in so many ways.

-Thanks to my father's Uncle Bill, who encouraged me to turn my rough manuscript into this book, and for introducing this story to his chaplain friends in the VA system.

-Thank you Dad (George) for many lessons while being the child of a kind-hearted man. I have learned from your wounds.

Once Home, your network of support is an essential part of healing your wounds. There are others like you, find them. Reach out to the VA, claim what you need to heal. You are supported. You are needed.

There are many resources available, here are a few:

www.mentalhealth.va.gov
www.acceptingtheashes.net
www.opuspeace.org
www.woundedwarriorproject.org
www.besselvanderkolk.com

ABOUT THE AUTHOR

Quynn Elizabeth Red Mountain (Red Mountain was a name given to Quynn's father by the Vietnamese people with whom he worked) is a Pastoral Counselor in the Animist tradition (All is connected in the Web of Life) and Soul Restoration practitioner.

Find out more about her soul tending services at https://acceptingtheashes.net/soul-restoration/

Made in the USA
Middletown, DE
28 September 2021

49117814R00040